WARRIORS TALK, INC. PRESENTS

WHEN WARRIORS TALK
MIRACLES HAPPEN

The Results of Letting God Lead

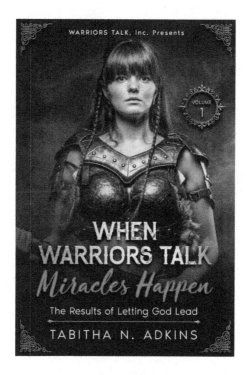

FEATURING

WARRIOR TABITHA N. ADKINS

Published by Warriors Talk, Inc.

www.warriorstalk.org

ISBN: 978-0-578-85308-6

Printed in the United States of America

Edited by: MyLeah Symone with Majestically Written Editing Services at www.majesticallymyleah.com

Cover designed by: Germancreative

Dedication

This book is dedicated to all of the Warriors who have encountered the horrific beast that is called cancer. It is comforting to know that giants (even in the form of a diagnosis,) do fall. It is my prayer that your days be filled with unspeakable JOY and that God will grant you with the strength to take out any giant that comes your way.

Rebecca,
I don't think you
understand how much
your "mermaid" refocused
me, and allowed me to Be the
best family member, friend, mom,
and mermaid I could Be!

xoxo
Yalitha Adkins ♡

Table of Contents

INTRODUCTION OF WARRIOR

TABITHA N. ADKINS

Warriors Talk, Inc. would like to present: Warrior Tabitha N. Adkins. She is an amazing survivor, fighter and conqueror. She is the true definition of a champion fighter who masters the ring, who never backs down and who brings home the victory in every round with God in her corner. Tabitha is a mother, daughter, and friend who has learned to appreciate the core relationships in her life. As a Warrior, Tabitha has battled many challenges, but she continues to fight with God directing every battle she faces. Tabitha is a walking miracle who displays how an all-powerful and intentional God shows up in her life over and over again. Facing Type 1 Diabetes, breast cancer and stage III kidney disease has challenged Tabitha physically, mentally, spiritually and financially. But, her obstacles have also developed her into the Warrior she is today. The battles have made her stronger, wiser, and more grateful. She now knows that God was preparing her to be a Warrior since birth and He is equipping her to be able to withstand the blows of the enemy.

Author's Notes

Living with cancer brings on emotions that NO ONE will ever understand unless you are currently going through it or you have already gone through it. It is emotionally exhausting, and it is painful. It makes you feel like a failure. Every day is a battle to wake up and love. And what is it to love about CANCER?

Cancer makes you appreciate every moment in life. Cancer makes you question every ache and pain that you feel. Cancer causes you to wonder: when you lay down at night, will you wake up in the morning? Cancer makes you feel weak and leaves you wondering. Cancer also makes you: HUMBLE, THANKFUL, and GRATEFUL. My battle with cancer has encouraged me to fight for those that are fighting, have fought and those that have lost their battle with cancer.

I've heard the saying, "God will not give you more than you can handle." I must be honest: I have questioned if God has me confused with someone else because of all I've gone through in my life. I sometimes think that I cannot handle any more, but God shows up and shows out every time. My story is not an easy one to stomach. Grab your glass of wine, beer, twisted tea, or your cup of coffee, and a tissue and join me as I share the short version of my testimony.

~ Chapter 1~

A Warrior is Born

It all started when I was younger as I watched my mom and dad deal with issues at home. To the outside world we were the perfect family with both parents, me, my two brothers and a dog. To the world we had it all, until my dad got hurt working in the coal mines and the doctors kept prescribing him pain pills. Once the sole breadwinner for my family, my dad began became addicted to the pills and an alcoholic to fill the void of not being able to work anymore. I watched my mom work her life away as a waitress to make ends meet, while my dad self-medicated his pain with substance abuse. It was not long after that when he started becoming abusive to my mom and my brothers.

Despite this, my mom became the strongest woman I've ever seen even though she was becoming emotionally, physically, and mentally drained. This continued for what seemed like a lifetime, until we escaped. We left the house in the middle of the night and went into hiding away from my father. When I was seven years old, things started to change for me. I started not feeling well. I had dark circles under my eyes. I lost weight and started drinking anything that I could get ahold of. My mom took me to the doctor, and I overheard the doctor say to my mom, "I think she has diabetes." After many tests and screenings, I was officially diagnosed with Type I diabetes. As a seven-year-old, I did not realize what this included or how my life would change forever. I was admitted to the hospital for eleven days and I remember crying because I knew that this was serious. I did not, however, realize exactly how serious it was.

After being released from the hospital, I took diabetes like a champ. I started giving myself injections of insulin and I began to come to terms with the changes occurring in my life. My life consisted of daily injections, diet modifications, and other daily stresses. I remember wanting to be like the other kids and not have to do the things that was required for my day to day life. I remember asking God. "Why me? Why did I have to go through this? If I ignored it, would it go away?"

When I was twenty-one years old, my life turned upside down when I was told that I was pregnant with my first child. I'd had miscarriages in the past and was told by the doctors that I would never be able to have a child because of my diabetes diagnosis. Even with this issue, I was on cloud nine knowing that I would have a tiny person in my life that would call me mom. After countless doctors' appointments and complications with the pregnancy, I gave birth to my son at twenty-five weeks gestation. When my baby was two days old, I got to hold him for the first time. Later that day, he had a grade three brain hemorrhage from being so small and over stimulated. The doctor came in to tell me that my baby was not going to make it through the night. I immediately stopped everything and asked God again, "Why me? Why do my precious baby and I have to go through this?" My baby lived and thrived through the night. He was able to come home three months later. God showed up and showed out. God was adding to my testimony again.

The following year, I became pregnant with my second child. It was at my first appointment that I found out my kidneys were failing. Because of this and my other health issues, the doctors told me that I should not have children. I questioned God over and over throughout this process. I struggled as my feet swelled and the swelling continued throughout my body. Over the next eight months, my blood pressure spiked up and the swelling continued.

Even with all the health issues, I delivered a healthy baby girl at thirty-six weeks. My life felt complete. I had all my dreams and prayers answered. I now had a boy and girl, but the condition of my kidneys worsened. I was then diagnosed with stage three kidney disease related to the diabetes and the pregnancy. Why did I have to go through this? I bargained with God, praying for him to heal me because I wanted to see my kids grow up. I pleaded with Him and promised that I would be the best mother that I could be. Even though I questioned God in this season, I was so happy to have my babies. I believe that they changed my life for the better. It was because of these two babies that I knew I had to make my life better for me and them. Nicholas and Kaitlyn became my reason for everything. I pray every day thanking God for them.

~ Chapter 2 ~
God's Plan

When I was thirty-five years old, God reminded me that His plan is better than any plan that I had for myself. The day after my birthday, I woke up with a bruise on my shoulder that would not go away. Several weeks later, I had an appointment with my gynecologist for my yearly exam. I asked her to look at the bruise even though it did not have anything to do with the reason that I was there. She commented that she did not feel anything but that she was going to send me in for a mammogram and ultrasound to make sure.

Because I was a thirty-five-year-old with no family history of breast cancer, my insurance had an issue with approving the mammogram. I prayed that it would be nothing more than a bruise. I was still young. I had too many things left that I wanted to accomplish for it to be anything other than just a bruise.

Within a few weeks, I had a mammogram scheduled. I walked into the breast cancer center with my head held high. I knew that I would have signs if it was the big C because I'd seen it on television. There would be a knot, a lump, or something that would be noticeable.

I always cringed when I saw the pink ribbon or when October came around and all you heard about was breast cancer. I knew that I did not have breast cancer. I was convinced that it was something simple. As I sat there, I watched women get called back for their appointments. Some of them left the appointment with tears in their eyes while some came out with big smiles on their faces. Some of them seemly disappeared.

I talked to God, wondering why these ladies had tears in their eyes, what happened behind those closed doors and what was about to happen to me? Then, my name was called, and I walked down what felt like the green mile in my paper gown. All the horror stories that I heard about the mammogram was about to come true. To my surprise, after my mammogram I was told that everything looked good. But I still needed to get an ultrasound done. Even then, I had faith that everything was going to be okay. After the ultrasound, the doctor was called in to examine my results more closely. Again, I found myself asking God, "Why me? What now?"

The doctor explained to me that I needed a biopsy that day. The doctor told me that what he saw appeared to be breast cancer. Because he wanted to be sure he would my results to pathology and he would call in a few days with the updated results. I must admit that those couple days of waiting for the results felt like an eternity. While I waited, I went to the library and got every book that I could find about breast cancer. After reading those books, I decided that I did not have any of the signs or symptoms that were in the books.

During the waiting, I prayed to God and reminded him that I had two kids and a lot more that I needed to accomplish. On November 16th, 2016 I got the phone call that I never anticipated on receiving while I was shopping at Target. The doctor confirmed that my biopsy came back and that I had breast cancer. I immediately stopped the buggy I was pushing. Did the doctor have my test mixed up with one of the other ladies that was there that day? I pleaded with God: this could not be my results.

When I left the store, I reminded God that I was only thirty-five and that my kids were only twelve and fourteen years old. I still had a lot of things that I had not had the opportunity to do. I had not traveled the world or experienced visiting a beach. I just knew that this result was wrong. I decided that the doctor would realize that these were not the correct results at my next appointment.

A week later at my appointment, I was told that my cancer was ER, PR+, HER2- and it was spreading. The doctor gave me several different scenarios and the common factor to all those scenarios was that I was going to lose my breast. It is hard to explain exactly how I felt after hearing this. Again, I found myself asking God, "Why me?"

On January 3, 2017, I had a double mastectomy after multiple tests and scans. I realized how much my life had changed when they initially took the bandages off three days later. I cried and could not understand why God was doing this to me. What did I do to deserve this? My smile immediately turned into a frown. Over the next few weeks, I had many conversations with God and waited for an answer. After getting the pathology results back from the surgery, I was told that I had no family history of cancer, and that my cancer was solely hormonal due to my birth control. The doctor informed me that chemo would not be a good option because it would make the kidney disease worse. The problem was: I had cancer in my lymph nodes.

I decided to get another opinion and do my research. I read a ton of books and talked to several doctors before deciding on fifty-four radiation treatments and tamoxifen.

This treatment plan seemed like the best option until I got lymphedema in my left side after having the lymph nodes removed. My surgeon had never seen this happens so quickly, and I did not recall reading anything about this in the books I'd read. I had my drains taken out and put back in four times before being sent to a lymphedema specialist in my area. I was not prepared for this and I did not know what to expect. I felt like I had my soul taken from me. How would I ever be the same person again?

Martina, my sister and best friend, overcame leukemia and experienced the same side effects that I was experiencing. She came to visit me after my surgery. We stayed up all night with a bottle of wine; we talked about our wishes, dreams and what we wanted for our children. We cried, we laughed and at the end of the conversation she challenged me to start asking "Why not me?" It was at that moment that I was prepared for battle. I truly felt the warrior in me. I allowed God to slow me down and listen to His plan for me instead of telling Him my plans.

It's funny how the spotlight showed me the people that were there when I needed them the most. I am grateful for Martina, Angie, Trisha, Toni, Bridgette, Veronica, Kitty (my mom,) and my babies Kaitlyn and Nicholas. They helped me find my purpose and my new beauty.

It was after the conversation with Martina that I started seeing the testimony in the test that I had been through. Those mentioned above helped me with dinners, laundry, running the kids around, and most importantly they allowed me to cry and laugh about everything. It's incredible that they were there for me every step of the way and I truly feel that God hand-picked each one of them for my life.

~ Chapter 3 ~
God, I have questions!

Let's fast forward to the end of May that same year. I'd been to many appointments to deal with the issues with my initial surgery. I was officially done with radiation and healing from the mastectomy. Tamoxifen was started and the decision was made that I would not have reconstruction done because of the complications that I experienced. I was happy with the new me, no bra was necessary.

The encouraging words of those who had the reconstruction surgery had never looked more appealing than they did at that moment. Who would have thought that things could change so quickly, without a warning? I credit my sister Martina for guiding me in the direction of seeking healing from God. I trusted that He was with me the entire time. However, I also questioned God often as to why He kept putting me through obstacles. Once I stated, "I beat breast cancer so what could be tougher than that?" Little did I know that I would soon find out.

My sister Martina received the news that her leukemia had come back and this time it came with a vengeance. After she received this news, we had another night of sitting and talking about things before she went back to the hospital. She let me know what her last wishes were and how bad things were going to get. Even in this struggle, she continued to remind me to ask God, "Why not me?"

A few months later, God called my sister home. She left me a letter to read after she passed and in it she reminded me that the biggest blessings in life are the moments that you share and the memories that you make with the individuals that you love. She also reminded me that there is no room for should've, would've or could've in our stories. We rode our friendship until the wheels fell off.

After countless tear-filled talks with God, I have been blessed with many memories of her and the ability to carry on her legacy every chance that I get. She told me to enjoy life and remember that God will show you who is meant to be in your life. She also told me to not be mad or upset with God because her work here was done, and then she proceeded to tell me that my work was just beginning. After reading this letter for the five hundredth time, I decided to talk to God and ask what was planned for me. How was I going to do it without my sister?

~ Chapter 4 ~

Why Not Me

God was not done molding me, even though I'd lost my breast, my sister, and now what? Just when I thought it couldn't get any worst, I started having side effects of the tamoxifen medication. I had a thickening and cysts forming on my uterus, along with a few abnormal cells present. I was sent to several doctors that gave me the news that I needed a hysterectomy. Here I am, two years later, with no breast, no uterus, and no cervix. I was on hormonal blockers that were meant to keep my cancer from coming back.

I had to pull my letter back out from Martina and read those words again. I had to be reminded that I needed to be asking, "Why not me?" God showed me why me when I stopped asking. I have had the opportunity to model for a calendar, I've been on television and I've been on radio shows. I traveled to New York, Utah, Florida, Virginia, Ohio, Pennsylvania, Texas, South Carolina, North Carolina, Hawaii, Cancun, and the Dominican Republic. I have met some of the most incredible women while being a representative of the breast cancer community. I did not see it at the time, but I see it now: God was preparing me for my battle over the years. There were times when I thought I was being tested; I now know that God was preparing my testimony. Every obstacle was another item added to my warrior story.

It is when we are silent, and we listen that we truly get exposed to God's message for us. I had to stop telling God my plans and open the path for God to show me His plans for me. This warrior talked and God surely listened to every word. Going through heartbreak and doubtful questions helped me get to the point where I can say that I understand and that I am ready for every challenge that lies ahead of me.

I would not be telling the truth if I said that I don't sometimes ask God "Why me?" I recently received the news that my kidneys are failing, and I only have a little bit of function left. I thought all was going to be fixed when I was referred to the kidney transplant doctor. This was not the case. Instead, I found out that because of the type of breast cancer I had and the likelihood of reoccurrence, I cannot be added to the transplant list until I am five years cancer free. I have two years to go. So, until that point, I will be on dialysis.

My life seems to be turned upside down once again. However, I know that God had the right individuals picked out to be in my life and that they will be riding this life with me until the wheels fall off. I know that my testimony is amazing, and that God is not done working on my life. I know that I am a warrior and that God has incredible plans for my life. I was born a warrior and after allowing God to guide my life and letting him take control, He truly has allowed me to share my story with others all over the globe.

"*I'm a survivor – a living example of what people can go through and survive.*"

~ Elizabeth Taylor

"Find a group of people who challenge and inspire you, spend a lot of time with them, and it will change your life."

~ Amy Poehler

Together we fight

"If you want to lift yourself up, lift up someone else."

~ Booker T. Washington

"When you look into your mother's eyes, you know that is the purest love you can find on this earth."

~Mitch Albom

Our Sisterhood

#Ourbond

#Always

~ Chapter 5 ~

Battled Tested

"Friendship is born at the moment when one person says to another, What! You too? I thought I was the only one."

-C.S. Lewis

"Lots of people want to ride in the limo, but what you want is someone who will take the bus with you when the limo breaks down."

-Oprah Winfrey

I hope you have refilled your glass and that you have tissues handy. In this chapter I am going to share some things that have helped me find my testimony in the many tests that I have faced throughout my life. This information is going to be helpful regardless of the reason that you picked up this book. This is for if you are newly diagnosed with something that has you questioning your faith, if you are a caregiver for another individual, and if you are a survivor looking for encouragement to get you to the next step of your journey. This is for you if you are simply looking for information to help a loved one that has not entered your life yet; I promise that this will leave your heart happy.

The first thing that you will need to help you through any situation is a relationship with God. He is always the first one that we want to call on when things are bad, but the last one that we want to build a relationship with when things are good. I suggest that you work on this relationship daily by scheduling time with God. Put it on the calendar just like you would with a hair appointment or a party.

I was always in church as a child, but it was not until I went through my breast cancer diagnosis that I worked on making my relationship with God stronger. Prior to my breast cancer diagnosis, a lot of so-called friends were around when the bars were open, or the food was free. Not long after I asked God to show me who my true friends were that I received my breast cancer diagnosis. Then, my so-called friends started to disappear because they did not want to be around when things get rough. Losing those people showed me how important it is to have a support system.

A support system can be made up of friends and family. For me, outside of my mom and a few of my cousins, my biggest supporters have been my friends (a.k.a. my sisters.) My friends showed up and showed out during this time. These women that had never personally gone through a breast cancer diagnosis did not leave my side through any of it. They helped with dinner, taking my kids to practice, washing clothes, taking me to appointments and picking up prescriptions.

Most importantly, these women let me be mad, ask questions, cry and they prayed with me. None of them told me to call if I needed something because they knew me. They knew that I would never pick up that phone and ask for anything because I believed that I was a strong and independent woman. They arranged dinners for my family, often sharing a list among them with things that needed to be done daily. My friends made sure that I did not have to worry about anything except getting better. Something that you can take away from the example of my friends is to: not just offer help but to just do it. We all know that an individual who is going through sickness needs to eat. We know that if there are children in the house that there are responsibilities that come with parenting that may be too much to do on your own if you are struggling with a diagnosis. And even though when we offer help it may be coming from a good place; we need to actually be willing to help out and make someone's load a little lighter.

Something that I have experienced over and over again is people telling me "My grandma had breast cancer and she is fine." This statement drives individuals that are going through a cancer diagnosis crazy. I am an individual that is learning my new normal and learning that every person with a cancer diagnosis will have a different story. I know that each diagnosis will be different, the treatment will be different, and their emotional perceptions will be different. Everyone will have different stories about their journey. Instead of telling someone with a cancer diagnosis that you know someone who was sick: allow them to express their fears, share their concerns and allow them to talk without responding.

~ Chapter 6 ~

My New Norm

Lord knows that with any diagnosis that things are going to change. Please remember that it is okay to get mad, to cry and to question why this is happening to you. Some of these changes no one could ever prepare you for.

For me, some of those changes looked like not knowing that I would need to buy bathing suits with removable padding in order to look normal after my mastectomy. No one could brace me for the day that I got my breast cancer diagnosis. No one prepared me for the time when I cried as the doctors took my dressings off after my mastectomy. No one prepared me for what "hot flashes" really felt like when I started on the tamoxifen or how they would come back with a vengeance after the hysterectomy. No one prepared me for how good a cold ginger ale would taste after a radiation treatment. It is so important to find at least one person that has had a similar diagnosis to talk to and support you as you experience these "new normal" on your journey.

When I first was diagnosed with breast cancer, I started searching for anything that I could find online to educate me and support me through this process. From my online search I found the *Send Me On Vacation Organization*. As I read the description of their programs and what they offered, I also filled out the applications for other organizations to help me with paying bills. I took all of these to my oncologist to have signed and I dropped them in the mail. That night, I remember crying and asking God, "Why did I continue to have horrible things happening to me?" I wanted to know what His plan was, and I wondered why He felt that I could handle this. How was I supposed to put on a brave face in front of my kids and tell them that everything was going to be okay? Deep down in my heart I was scared and unsure of what was going to happen. I cried for hours that night until I finally fell asleep.

The next day I woke up with the feeling that everything was going to be fine. I got a check in the mail that day for enough money to pay my electric bill. Two weeks later, I received a phone call from a number that I did not recognize. Cathy, the founder of *Send Me On Vacation*, pulled me in with her vibrant and energetic voice when she offered me a vacation. She then asked if I could be at the airport the following Saturday. I hesitated and told her that I would love to go but that I couldn't afford the trip. She told me that wouldn't be a problem because the trip was free of charge and all inclusive. Cathy reassured me that *Send Me On Vacation* would take care of everything, so I agreed to go on the trip. I had no idea what I just agreed to at the time. All I know is that I was excited and nervous at the same time. Everything seemed legit with the trip offer, so that following Saturday I went to the airport and headed to another country with six ladies that I never met before in my life for a seven-day vacation. Little did I know that my life would be changed in those seven days and a new person would return home to my family and friends.

During that week, I truly found the purpose of my journey and God let me know that everything that I had been through had happened for a reason. My experience at the Lifestyle Holidays vacation resort in the Dominican Republic was truly one to remember. They catered to my every need and gave me an outlet to recharge.

During my week vacation, myself and the other ladies laughed and cried together. We shared our scars, our visions and our hopes. My biggest take away from my experience is that I gained six sisters that I will forever share my transformation into a mermaid with. Yes, you read that correctly: we turned into mermaids. On the trip, our breast cancer journey was compared to the magical journey of a mermaid. We discussed how even in troubled waters, there is a beauty that is added to you through the journey.

At the end of the week, we had a complete mermaid makeover and a photo shoot. That process reminded me that I may not have my breast and I may not be the same woman that I once was, but I still am a majestic, powerful and beautiful woman. I will forever be grateful to Cathy, her husband, and all of my pink sister mermaids at *Send Me On Vacation*.

"I may not be the same woman that I once was, but I still am a majestic, powerful and beautiful woman."

~Tabitha Adkins

"You have been assigned this mountain to show others it can be moved."

Mel Robbins

~ Chapter 7 ~

When Your Support

System ROCKS!

If you take anything from this chapter, please remember that finding a support group to be there for you during your journey is essential. Regardless of where you are in your journey, looking up opportunities like *Send Me On Vacation* will benefit you greatly.

If you have a moment to check out their website for more information and to help support future mermaids, do so at www.sendmeonvacation.org. My support system has helped me to become the best version of myself. Through my close circle and opportunities, I have had, I have learned to trust God to direct me to the people and places that I need in my life. Keep in mind that your support system and outlets may look different from mine. We are all individuals who are unique, and we have to find what works best for us. For me, the most important part of my support system is God. God truly is the first one I talk to in the morning and last person that I talk to every night. My relationship with God is a work in progress and it has not always been the best, but thankfully He is a forgiving God and still guides me even when I am questioning Him. Another essential part of my close circle are my friends who I call my sisters. My sisters are there for me through thick and thin. They are not mere acquaintances.

These are the people in my life that know what is going on and they are able to give me advice. Everyone should have a support system that is there to listen when you need to talk and be a shoulder to cry on. In my life, I have my core originals. These are the ladies that have seen me at my worst, at my best and they have supported me through all of it. One thing for sure, it does not matter how much time there is before we get together again. We pick up right where we left off. This group of ladies includes: Trisha, Toni, Bridgette and Angie. They go above and beyond and definitely help give me the strength to keep going. I love them so much and am thankful that they have helped me to see the beauty in myself and for being my spiritual sisters. They inspire me and remind me constantly that prayer changes things.

Deshaunda, Veronica, Crystal, Pam, and Aimee are the ladies who have come into my life throughout the years. They are always there to support me, cry with me, laugh with me and then tell me to get back up and straighten my crown. Then, there is Magen and Denikah, who are not close in distance, but are only a phone call away. Even though we are not with each other all of the time, we are always there.

To all of the ladies mentioned: Thank you for loving me, even when I was not the best at loving you back. I want to say thank you for being my mentors, my secret keepers, my partners in crime, my voices of reason, my protectors, my best friends, and most of all my sisters. I will always rock with you.

I have to give a BIG thank you to my sister and best friend Martina. She truly taught me how to be compassionate towards others, to love everyone through their faults and to always give second chances. When God decided that her battle was over and called her home, I stayed strong like she would have wanted me to do. However, a part of my heart left with her that day. There will forever be a void inside me that I cannot express. I miss her daily phone calls and most of all I miss her loving hugs. If you are reading this and have the opportunity to do so, please reach out to *bethematch.org* so that you can help keep Martina's legacy alive by being a bone marrow donor. For the rest of my life, I will strive to be half the inspiration to others that Martina has been to me.

"They are always there to support me, cry
with me, laugh with me and then tell me to
get back up and straighten my crown."

~ Tabitha Adkins

I want to thank God for my children, Nicholas and Kaitlyn. They are my everything. They have encouraged me so much to keep a smile on my face and to keep fighting. I just want them to know that I may not always be able to do everything that I want to do for them, but I will never stop trying. My children were young teenagers when I went through my breast cancer journey. They have seen me through my good days and my bad days. I would cry and ask God to just give me the strength to be the best mother that I could be and to help me to not show my kids how scared I was. That is exactly what God did.

"They are my everything"

Lastly, I have to give a special thank you to my parents: Kitty, Tom, Wally and Lora. You guys do not know how much I appreciate everything that you have done for the kids and me. I love you all and appreciate the influence that each of you have had on my life. Thank you for helping me be the best I can be.

Now, you might be thinking, "Now what?" Well, I am in the process of starting a new chapter in my life with dialysis. I currently have no evidence of disease as far as my breast cancer diagnosis, and my diabetes is a daily journey in itself. Please keep praying for me and for my family and I will definitely be praying for you.

To my friends, family, and the individuals reading this book: live this life by making each day better ON PURPOSE! Live, love, laugh, and leave a legacy!

God Bless! -XOXO, Tabitha

IT CAME.

I FOUGHT.

I WON.

Tabitha N. Adkins is a breast cancer survivor and thriver. She is a first-time author and a comedian. She is an active team leader for the *Send Me On Vacation* organization, where she educates about focusing on helping to restore inner healing and finding beauty in the new normal after a breast cancer diagnosis. She also sits as Vice President and Co-founder for the *Strong Sistahood-N-Pink Foundation.* This foundation helps individuals in West Virginia diagnosed with breast cancer with transportation, medication, and utility assistance while they are going through treatment.

Tabitha has been invited all over the US to speak, emcee, and facilitate workshops on the importance of knowing your normal and early detection. She has received her L.P.N., BA in psychology and MA in counseling. She achieved all of this while managing type 1 diabetes, kidney disease, beating a breast cancer diagnosis, and being a single mother of two amazing children.

She looks forward to sharing more about her experiences to help you find the humor in the struggles and the strengths of your current situation.

Connect with Tabitha

Tadkins250@yahoo.com

www.Facebook.com/tabitha.adkins.50.

SMOV- sendmeonvacation.org

About WARRIORS TALK, Inc.

Warriors Talk, Inc. NFP Est. 2014

Warriors Talk, Inc. was created in October 2014 by Lady Reshelle. She began using her testimony to encourage, educate, and empower individuals. She continues to do this through the *Warriors Talk* platform, where she promotes taking action for a healthier lifestyle before, during, and after a cancer diagnosis.

The Weekly Radio Broadcast

Going into its sixth year, *The Warriors Talk Radio Broadcast* covers a variety of topics on air. Topics covered on the show include: how cancer and other diseases are running rampant throughout our country. The motto on the show is, "MOVING FROM AWARENESS TOWARDS ACTION." Listeners walk away feeling empowered, informed, and connected to not only survive but also thrive in life. The broadcast consists of interviews with Warriors who are in battle, survivors, doctors, nurses, researchers and more. Many use the broadcast as a weekly support group that they can attend from the comfort of their homes every Monday at 6 p.m. CST on Facebook LIVE (@warriorstalk1 or on www.intellectualradio.com.)

Annual Survivors Night of Reflection Gala

On October 19 of 2019, *Warriors Talk Inc.* celebrated its fourth annual **Survivors Night of Reflection Gala**. This event allows survivors to reflect on their journey, express their gratitude for life, and share their wisdom after conquering cancer. The gala is not only for survivors but for those Warriors who are currently in battle as well. Funds raised go to the **Warriors In The Battle Fund**. The purpose of the fund is to provide financial assistance to individuals who are fighting cancer, so that they can concentrate on the fighting and healing process.

Battle Buddy Sacs

A portion of the funds are also used for **Battle Buddy Sacs**. These sacs are put together with items handpicked and distributed to cancer centers throughout the Chicagoland area (as well as the surrounding suburbs.) The sacs contain items that help to reduce stress, calm fears, and document the Warrior's journey.

Annual Paint & Dip

Fighting cancer is no easy task. Many Warriors rarely get a moment to enjoy the little things in life. This fun event was created to give the Warrior in battle a sense of serenity while on their cancer journey. Each Warrior has the opportunity to create their own masterpiece while releasing some of the stress associated with fighting cancer.

Connect with Warriors Talk, Inc.

Facebook, Twitter & Instagram: @warriorstalk1

YouTube: Warriors Talk w/Lady ReShell

Website: www.warriorstalk.org

Email: warriorstalk1@gmail.com

Also Published by Warriors Talk, Inc.

Warriors Talk, God Listens is a tell-all collection of cancer journeys from previvor, co-survivors, survivors and thrivers. The authors take you on their journey as they come face to face with their Goliath experience. This encounter tested them on every level, attempting to deplete their strength, faith, sanity and end their lives. Just as David did, they put on the whole armor of God and were successful at slaying their Giant. Sometimes you are weighed down with the pressures of life, rendering you helpless but just one encounter with God can change the trajectory of your journey.

2020 Artists Promoting Success Award-Winner

Visions of Happiness is a book of poems that takes you on life transformations from pleasure and pain to purpose. This journey will allow you to take on life's trials, tribulations and celebrations, and transform them into visions with purpose. As the reader, you will be able to travel back in time and venture off into this turbulent journey of happiness.

Warriors Talk Publishing

Established in 2019

www.warriorstalk.org

Made in the USA
Middletown, DE
25 April 2021